FOCUS **ON**

MIDDLE SCHOOL

GRADES 5-8

PHYSICS

Teacher's Manual
3rd Edition

Rebecca W. Keller, PhD

Real Science-4-Kids

Focus On Middle School Physics Teacher's Manual—3rd Edition
ISBN 978-1-941181-75-1

Published by Gravitas Publications Inc.
www.gravitaspublications.com
www.realscience4kids.com

A Note from the Author

This curriculum is designed to engage middle school level students in further exploration of the scientific discipline of physics. The *Focus On Middle School Physics Student Textbook—3rd Edition* and the accompanying *Laboratory Notebook* together provide students with basic science concepts needed for developing a solid framework for real science investigation into physics.

The experiments in the *Laboratory Notebook* allow students to expand on concepts presented in the *Student Textbook* and develop the skills needed for using the scientific method. This *Teacher's Manual* will help you guide students through the laboratory experiments.

There are several sections in each chapter of the *Laboratory Notebook*. The section called *Think About It* provides questions to help students develop critical thinking skills and spark their imagination. The *Experiment* section provides students with a framework to explore concepts presented in the *Student Textbook*. In the *Conclusions* section students draw conclusions from the observations they have made during the experiment. A section called *Why?* provides a short explanation of what students may or may not have observed. And finally, in each chapter an additional experiment is presented in *Just For Fun*.

The experiments take up to 1 hour. Materials needed for each experiment are listed on the following pages and also at the beginning of each experiment.

Enjoy!

Rebecca W. Keller, PhD

Materials at a Glance

Experiment 1	Experiment 2	Experiment 4	Experiment 5	Experiment 7
tennis ball paperclip yarn or string (about 3 meters [10 ft]) marble bouncing ball, 1 (or 2 or more of different sizes) **Optional** penknife, ice pick, awl, or other sharp tool pliers	electronic circuit kit (see next page **Other**) **Experiment 3** Slinky several paperclips 1-2 apples 1-2 lemons or limes 1-2 oranges 1-2 bananas spring balance scale or food scale meterstick, yardstick, or tape measure tape	small to medium size toy car stiff cardboard wooden board, smooth and straight (more than 1 meter [3 feet] long) straight pin or tack, several small scale or balance one banana, sliced 10 pennies meterstick, yardstick or tape measure tape	student-selected materials several sheets of paper **Experiment 6** several glass marbles of different sizes several steel marbles of different sizes cardboard tube, .7-1 meter [2.5-3 ft] long scissors black marking pen ruler letter scale or other small scale or balance	stopwatch compass an open space large enough to run (park, schoolyard, playground, backyard, etc.) 5 markers of students' choice to mark distances blank paper a group of friends

Experiment 8	Experiment 9	Experiment 10	Experiment 11	Experiment 12
pencil or pen marking pen thumbtack or pushpin 3 pieces of string — approximate sizes: 10 cm [4 in.]; 15 cm [6 in.]; 20 cm [8 in.] tape ruler (metric) large piece of white paper (bigger than 30 cm [12 in.] square — students may need to tape several sheets of paper together) firm surface at least as large as the paper and that a thumbtack can be pinned into	10-20 copper pennies (pennies made before 1982 have more copper and work best) aluminum foil paper towels salt water: 30-45 ml (2-3 Tbsp.) salt per 240 ml (1 cup) water voltmeter* 2 plastic-coated copper wires, each 10-15 cm (4"-6") long duct tape (or other strong tape) scissors wire cutters fine steel wool, plain (no soap), 1 pad 9 volt battery ovenproof pan or dish heatproof pad or surface **Optional** wire stripping tool bucket of water	small glass jar with lid aluminum foil (small piece) paperclip duct tape (or other strong tape) plastic or rubber rod (or balloon) silk fabric (or can use hair with a balloon) scissors ruler awl or other tool to make a hole several thin, bendable plastic straws (thick straws may not work well) paper tissues (Kleenex) or cloth made of silk or wool small piece of paper small piece of aluminum foil 1 or more books — thin pages preferable 1-2 plastic combs plastic cup shallow bowl or a plate	(2) D cell batteries and battery holder (2) 3.7 volt light bulbs and sockets (1) switch (4) alligator clip connectors (2) 5 ohm, 1/4 watt resistors (1) DC motor with propeller Materials are available as a kit from Home Science Tools (as of this writing): Product #: EL-KITBASC http://www.hometrainingtools.com/	metal rod (e.g., large nail 8.9 cm [3.5"] long, 16d flathead—or an unmagnetized screwdriver) electrical wire, .3-.6 meter (1'-2') 10-20 paperclips 6v or larger battery (12v battery if a screwdriver is used) electrical tape or 2 alligator clips scissors wire cutters bar magnet small plastic baggie small flat-bottomed clear plastic container with lid [about 5 cm x 8 cm x 1.5 cm (2" x 3" x 1/2")—a box straight pins come in would work] clear Karo syrup spoon 2 pencils or other props **Optional** wire stripping tool iron filings**

* An inexpensive voltmeter can be purchased at any store that supplies electrical equipment. Make sure the voltage scale is low enough to detect small voltages. A typical penny-cell produces about 0.5v.

** Available from Home Science Tools CH-IRON, http://www.hometrainingtools.com/

Materials
Quantities Needed for All Experiments

Equipment	Materials	Foods
alligator clip connector (2)[1]	aluminum foil	apple, 1-2
awl or other tool to make a hole	baggie, small plastic	banana, 2-3
ball, bouncing, 1 (or 2 or more of different sizes)	board, wooden, smooth and straight (more than 1 meter [3 feet] long)	Karo syrup, clear
ball, tennis	book, 1 or more — thin pages preferable	lemon or lime, 1-2
battery, 6v or larger (12v battery used with a screwdriver)	cardboard, stiff	orange, 1-2
battery, 9 volt	cardboard tube, .7-1 meter [2.5-3 ft] long	
battery, D cell (2) and battery holder[1]	comb, plastic, 1-2	
bowl, shallow, or a plate	cup, plastic	
compass	fabric, silk (or hair and a balloon)	
container with lid, small flat-bottomed clear plastic [about 5 cm x 8 cm x 1.5 cm (2" x 3" x 1/2") — a box straight pins come in would work]	markers of students' choice to mark distances, 5	
	materials, student-selected	
jar, small, glass with lid	paper, large piece, white (bigger than 30 cm [12 in.] square — can tape several sheets of paper together)	
light bulb, 3.7 volt (2), and sockets (2)[1]	paper, several sheets	
magnet, bar	paper towels	
marble, glass, several of different sizes	paperclips, 10-20	
marble, steel, several of different sizes	pen, black marking	
meterstick, yardstick, or tape measure	pencil or pen	
motor, DC, with propeller[1]	pencil, (2) or other props	
pad or surface, heatproof	rod, plastic or rubber (or balloon)	
pan or dish, ovenproof	salt water: 30-45 ml (2-3 Tbsp.) salt per 240 ml (1 cup) water	
pennies, 10	steel wool, fine, plain (no soap), 1 pad	
pennies, 10-20 copper (pennies made before 1982 have more copper and work best)	straws, plastic, thin, bendable, several (thick straws may not work well)	
	string, 3 pieces — approximate sizes: 10 cm [4 in.]; 15 cm [6 in.]; 20 cm [8 in.]	**Other**
resistor, 5 ohm, 1/4 watt, (2)[1]	tack or straight pin, several	
rod, metal (e.g., large nail 8.9 cm [3.5"] long, 16d flathead—or an unmagnetized screwdriver)	thumbtack or pushpin	electronic circuit kit (choose one):
	tissues, paper (Kleenex) or cloth made of silk or wool	Snap Circuits: http://www.snapcircuits.net/
ruler	tape	Snap Circuits Jr. 100 Kit
ruler (metric)	tape, duct (or other strong tape)	Little Bits: http://littlebits.cc/intro
scale, letter, or other small scale or balance	wire, electrical, .3-.6 meter (1'-2')	Base Kit: http://littlebits.cc/kits/base-kit
scale, spring balance or food	wire, plastic-coated copper wires, 2 pieces, each 10-15 cm (4"-6") long	Note: If these products are no longer available, do an internet search on children's electronic circuit kits to find a kit suitable for this experiment.
scissors	yarn or string (about 3 meters [10 ft])	
Slinky		
spoon	**Optional**	group of friends
stopwatch		
switch, electric[1]	iron filings[2]	open space large enough to run (park, schoolyard, playground, backyard, etc.)
toy car, small to medium size	tape, electrical	
voltmeter*		surface, firm, large, that a thumbtack can be pinned into
wire cutters		
Optional		
bucket		
penknife, ice pick, awl, or other sharp tool		
pliers		
wire stripping tool		

[1] Electrical materials are available as a kit from Home Science Tools (as of this writing): Product #: EL-KITBASC
  http://www.hometrainingtools.com/
[2] Available from Home Science Tools CH-IRON, http://www.hometrainingtools.com/

Contents

◇◇◇

Experiment 1   **It's the Law!**   1

Experiment 2   **Using Electronics**   5

Experiment 3   **Fruit Works?**   8

Experiment 4   **Smashed Banana**   13

Experiment 5   **On Your Own**   17

Experiment 6   **Moving Marbles**   20

Experiment 7   **Accelerate to Win!**   25

Experiment 8   **Around and Around**   31

Experiment 9   **Power Pennies**   36

Experiment 10   **Charge It!**   41

Experiment 11   **Circuits and Ohm's Law**   46

Experiment 12   **Wrap It Up!**   52

Experiment 1

It's the Law!

Materials Needed

- tennis ball
- paperclip
- yarn or string (about 3 meters [10 ft])
- marble
- bouncing ball, 1 (or 2 or more of different sizes)

Optional

- penknife, ice pick, awl, or other sharp tool
- pliers

Objectives

In this experiment students will be introduced to the concept of *physical laws*—a fundamental concept in physics.

The objectives of this lesson are for students to:

- Use the scientific method to observe the physical world.
- Explore Newton's First Law of Motion.

Experiment

I. Think About It

Read this section of the *Laboratory Notebook* with your students.

Ask the students what a law is, such as a law against driving too fast or a law against stealing. Ask if these laws can be broken and, if so, why they can be broken.

Explain that laws in physics differ from the kinds of laws that govern our country. In physics a law is an overall principle or relationship that remains the same and is not broken.

Ask the students to describe several observations they have made about how objects behave in the physical world. Encourage them to discuss as many observations as they can think of. There are no "right" answers, and at this point, it is not important to know the reasons why something happens.

Ask questions such as the following:

- *What happens when you put on the brakes while riding a bicycle? Do the tires stop immediately? Do they skid?*

- *What happens when you throw a ball into the air? Does it reach the clouds? Does it come down in the same spot?*

- *What happens when you turn on a flashlight? How far can you see the light? Can you see the beam from a flashlight in the daytime?*

- *Have you ever thrown a ball and had it not come down (except when it gets stuck somewhere like in a tree)?*

- *Does ice always float?*

- *Does the Sun always come up in the morning?*

II. Experiment 1: It's the Law!

Read this section of the *Laboratory Notebook* with your students.

In this experiment students will discover Newton's First Law of Motion by observing the movements of a tennis ball and a marble. Newton's First Law of Motion can be stated as:

A body will remain at rest or in motion until it is acted on by an outside force.

The objective is provided. Have the students read through the experiment and then write a hypothesis based on the steps of the experiment.

Part I

❶ Students are to observe how a ball travels through the air. They should notice that the ball will go up and come down in some kind of arc every time they throw it. The arc can be shallow or sharp depending on how they throw the ball.

Challenge them to throw the ball so that it won't come down.

Ask them if they can get the ball to go up and down in a pattern different from an arc.

❷ Have the students follow the directions to use a paperclip to attach the string to the tennis ball. It is somewhat difficult to puncture the tennis ball with the paperclip, so have students take care while doing this. You may want to first put a small hole in the tennis ball with a penknife, ice pick, or awl before having the students insert the paperclip.

Alternatively, a longer string can be used, wrapped several times around the ball, and secured with tape. It is harder to get the string to stay attached to the ball using this method.

❸ With the string attached, the trajectory of the tennis ball will be different. When the string has reached its full length, the ball will abruptly stop and fall to the ground.

Have the students throw the ball several times. Ask them if they can change how the ball falls to the ground. They should notice that if they shorten the string, the ball does not travel as far as when the string is longer. They should also notice that if they do not throw the ball very far and it does not reach the end of the string, the ball will travel almost as if there were no string attached to it.

Have them record their results.

Part II

❶ Students will roll a marble several times on a smooth surface and record their results.

❷ Students will roll a marble several times on a rough surface and record their results.

III. Conclusions

Have the students review the results they recorded for Part I and Part II of the experiment. Have them draw conclusions based on the data they collected.

IV. Why?

Read this section of the *Laboratory Notebook* with your students.
Discuss any questions that might come up.

V. Just For Fun

In this experiment students will play with a bouncing ball and observe how the amount of force used changes the way the ball bounces. With more force, the ball will bounce higher and more times.

If bouncing balls of different sizes are available, have the students repeat the experiment and observe whether the size of the ball affects the outcome.

Experiment 2

Using Electronics

Materials Needed

One of the following recommended electronic circuit kits:

- Snap Circuits: http://www.snapcircuits.net/
  Snap Circuits Jr. 100 Kit

- Little Bits: http://littlebits.cc/intro
  Base Kit: http://littlebits.cc/kits/base-kit

Note: Websites and product availability change over time. If these products are no longer available, do an internet search on children's electronic circuit kits to find a kit suitable for this experiment.

Objectives

In this experiment students will explore electric circuits.

The objectives of this lesson are for students to:

- Learn about basic electric circuits.
- Expand their understanding of electronics in science.

Experiment

I. Think About It

Read this section of the *Laboratory Notebook* with your students.

Ask questions such as the following to guide open inquiry.

- *What do you think your life would be like if there were no electric circuits?*
- *How do you think electric circuits have helped shape the modern world?*
- *How many different items can you name that have an electric circuit?*
- *If you could use electric circuits to create something new, what would you create?*

II. Experiment 2: Using Electronics

Have the students read the entire experiment before writing an objective and a hypothesis.

Objective: Have the students think of an objective for this experiment (what will they be learning?).

Hypothesis: Have the students write a hypothesis. The hypothesis can restate the objective in a statement that can be proved or disproved by their experiment. Some examples:

- *A basic electric circuit can be used to illuminate a light bulb.*
- *A basic electric circuit can be used to rotate a motor.*
- *Electric circuits can be combined*
- *Chemical energy in a battery can be converted to mechanical energy using an electric circuit.*

EXPERIMENT

One of the best ways to learn about electronics is to build electronic circuits. However, putting together electronic circuits can be difficult for most kids, so we recommend buying an electronic circuit kit. Students can then explore the various circuit combinations provided by the kit in a way that is easier for them to understand.

Select one of the electronics kits from the Materials List.

❶-❷ Have your students study the parts and read the instructions and the Do's and Don'ts. Make sure they have a good understanding of what the parts are and how to use them before they proceed with the projects.

❸-❹ Have your students assemble the first two projects in the kit, following the kit instructions. They will be learning more about electric circuits as they work through each project. In the spaces provided, have them record their observations, including a diagram of the finished project with the parts labeled and a description of how the completed project works. Have them note whether the project worked as described.

Making diagrams is an important part of scientific exploration. The diagrams can be sketches rather than realistically drawn since their purpose is to help students understand the projects they build.

Results

Now that the students have a basic understanding of the kit and electric circuits, have them assemble several different projects and record their observations, including labeled diagrams and a description of how each project works. By the time they finish the experiment, they should have a good understanding of the components, how they work, and how to put them together.

III. Conclusions

Have the students answer the questions and draw conclusions based on their observations. Help them determine whether their conclusions support or do not support their hypothesis..

IV. Why?

Read this section of the *Laboratory Notebook* with your students.
Discuss any questions that might come up.

V. Just For Fun

Students are asked to make a circuit of their own design and then record their observations, including a labeled diagram and a description of how it works.

Experiment 3

Fruit Works?

Materials Needed

- Slinky
- several paperclips
- 1-2 apples
- 1-2 lemons or limes
- 1-2 oranges
- 1-2 bananas
- spring balance scale or food scale
- meterstick, yardstick, or tape measure
- tape

Objectives

In this experiment students will be introduced to the fundamental concepts of force, energy, and work.

The objectives of this lesson are for students to:

- Gain a basic understanding of the concepts of force, energy, and work.
- Observe gravitational force acting on an object.

Experiment

I. Think About It

Read this section of the *Laboratory Notebook* with your students.

Have a discussion with the students concerning their own ideas about force, energy, and work. Ask questions such as the following to guide open inquiry.

- *What do you think work is?*
- *Do you think work is done if you move bricks from the front yard to the back yard? Why or why not?*
- *Do you think work is done if you lift a book? Why or why not?*
- *Do you think more work is done if you lift three books at the same time than if you lift one book? Why or why not?*
- *Is work done if a piece of fruit is dropped? Why or why not?*
- *What do you think force is?*
- *Can you give some examples of force?*

II. Experiment 3: Fruit Works?

Read this section of the *Laboratory Notebook* with your students.

In this experiment the students will try to determine how much work a variety of fruits can do. Remind the students that:

work = distance x force

Objective: Have the students read the entire experiment and then guide them to think of a possible objective. For example:

- *Using a Slinky, we will find out if a banana can do more work than an orange.*

- *We will measure the work that fruit can do.*

- *We will find out if two bananas do more work than one.*

Experiment

❶ Have the students "weigh" the pieces of fruit by picking them up. They should be able to tell which one is the heaviest and which is lightest just by feeling the weights of the different fruits in their hands. Have the students make a guess about which fruit will do more work and which will do the least.

❷ Have them state their theory as the hypothesis. For example:

- *A banana is heavier than a lemon and will do more work.*

- *The orange is lighter than the apple and will do less work.*

- *The apple and the orange weigh the same amount and will do the same amount of work.*

❸-❹ Have the students use a scale to weigh each piece of fruit and record the weight in the chart provided.

❺ Have the students make hooks from paperclips to attach the fruit to the Slinky. We found that the paperclips worked fairly well, but younger kids found tape easier to use. The fruit can be fixed to the Slinky in any manner. You might ask the students to come up with their own ideas for attaching the fruit.

❻ Students will have to experiment with the Slinky and the number of coils that hang down. We found that it worked fairly well to have a student hold most of the coils in their hand and allow only a few coils to fall below the hand. Also, instead of holding the Slinky, it can be attached to a branch of a tree or a fixed ledge of some sort. Just make sure the Slinky is free to extend and does not contact any other surface and that the Slinky is at the same distance from the floor each time.

❼ Have the students measure the distance from the floor to the bottom of the Slinky and record this number in the chart provided.

❽ Have the students attach a piece of fruit to the last coil of the Slinky, and allow the coils to extend.

❾ Have them measure the distance from the ground to the bottom of the Slinky for each piece of fruit that is tested and then record the distance in the chart provided.

❿ Have the students repeat Steps ❽ and ❾ with different kinds of fruit.

Results

❶ Have the students use the chart in Step ❾ of the previous section. They will subtract the distance from the floor to the Slinky without any fruit on it from the distance with the fruit on it. The result will be the distance the Slinky extended.

❷ Students will use the following equation to determine how much work was done by each piece of fruit: *work = distance x force* where force is the weight of the fruit.

Explain the measurement system the students are using:

When using the metric measurement system in the equation above, the unit of measure of work is the kilogram-meter. For example, 2 kilograms x 2 meters = 4 kilogram-meters of work. (A gram is equivalent to .001 kg.)

When using the British measurement system in the equation above, the unit of measure of work is the foot-pound. For example, 2 pounds x 2 feet = 4 foot-pounds of work. (An ounce is equivalent to .0625 lb.)

NOTE:

In this experiment weight and mass are being used interchangeably, even though they are not the same thing. Mass is the property that causes objects to have inertia. Mass and inertia will be discussed in a later book.

Technically, when we weigh something we are measuring its mass times the force of gravity (gravitational acceleration). Gravitational acceleration is equal to 1 and is the same everywhere on Earth. For this reason and for the purposes of this experiment we therefore use mass and weight interchangeably.

III. Conclusions

Have the students review the results they recorded for the experiment. Have them draw conclusions based on the data they collected.

IV. Why?

Read this section of the *Laboratory Notebook* with your students.
Discuss any questions that might come up.

V. Just For Fun

❶-❷ Have the students predict what would happen if they attached two bananas of about the same size or two other pieces of the same kind and similar size of fruit to the Slinky. They should predict that two pieces of fruit will do more work than one piece of fruit. Have them test this prediction by attaching two pieces of fruit to the Slinky and repeating the steps done previously. Have them record their results and then calculate the amount of work done. Have them analyze their results. Do two pieces of fruit do twice the work? Three times the work? Four times the work?

Smashed Banana

Materials Needed

- small to medium size toy car
- stiff cardboard
- wooden board, smooth and straight (more than 1 meter [3 feet] long)
- straight pin or tack, several
- small scale or balance
- one banana, sliced
- 10 pennies
- meterstick, yardstick or tape measure
- tape

Objectives

Performing this experiment will help students understand that energy exists in different forms, is converted from one form to another, and can do work.

The objectives of this lesson are for students to:

- Observe energy changing from one form to another.
- Use a formula to calculate gravitational potential energy.

Experiment

I. Think About It

Read this section of the *Laboratory Notebook* with your students.

Ask questions such as the following to guide open inquiry.

- *What do you think it would mean if someone said to you that you have the potential to become a famous scientist?*

- *What other examples of potential can you think of?*

- *What do you think gravitational potential energy is?*

- *Do you think gravitational potential energy can do work? Why or why not?*

- *What do you think kinetic energy is?*

- *Do you think gravitational potential energy and kinetic energy are the same or different? Why?*

II. Experiment 4: Smashed Banana

Read this section of the *Laboratory Notebook* with your students.

❶ Have the students read the entire experiment.

Objective: Have the students write an objective. Some examples:

- *We will measure how much GPE is needed to smash a banana.*

- *We will show that a heavier toy car needs less height (less GPE) to smash a banana.*

Hypothesis: Have the students write a hypothesis. For example:

> - *The toy car will not be able to smash the banana no matter how high the ramp.*
>
> - *The toy car will smash the banana when the ramp is two or three feet high.*
>
> - *The toy car is not big enough to smash the banana.*
>
> - *The toy car needs to have at least 50 pennies on it to smash the banana.*

❷-❸ Have the students assemble the apparatus according to the directions in the *Laboratory Notebook*. The experiment works best if the board is smooth and reasonably straight. A cardboard tube, such as a wrapping paper tube, also works if cut lengthwise and opened up to make a trough. The car should have good wheels and roll smoothly and easily to reduce friction.

When testing this experiment, we found that we needed to put several pieces of banana next to each other at the bottom of the ramp since the car often does not travel in a straight line.

❹ Have the students weigh the toy car and record the weight in the space provided.

❺-❼ Have the students elevate one end of the ramp 5 cm (2 inches) and roll the toy car down the ramp. Then have them elevate the ramp in 5 cm (2 inch) increments, allowing the car to travel down the ramp and hit the banana each time the ramp is raised. Have them record the results each time.

We found that an average toy car does not really smash the banana until the ramp has been elevated more than 30 cm (12 inches).

❽ Have the students answer the questions.

❾ The students will add pennies to the car to make it heavier. They may need to tape the pennies to the car. Have them weigh the car again with the pennies on it and repeat the experiment. They should discover that the ramp will not need to be elevated quite as high in order for the toy car to smash the banana.

❿ Have the students answer the questions.

Results

Have the students calculate the GPE for the toy car with and without the pennies at the corresponding heights at which the banana was smashed. The formula is:

gravitational potential energy (GPE) = weight x height

The GPEs should be roughly equal. Basically, we expect that it takes a given amount of KE (kinetic energy) to smash the banana, and it doesn't matter whether this comes in the form of a heavy, slow car or a light, fast car. The GPE the students calculate is the energy needed to smash the banana.

III. Conclusions

Have the students review the results they recorded for the experiment. Have them draw conclusions based on the data they collected.

IV. Why?

Read this section of the *Laboratory Notebook* with your students.
Discuss any questions that might come up.

V. Just For Fun

Have the students repeat the experiment using a raw egg instead of a banana. They should discover that it takes more force to break an egg than to smash a banana slice. The amount of force can be increased by raising the ramp and/or putting more weight on the car.

Experiment 5

On Your Own

Materials Needed

- student-selected materials
- several sheets of paper

Objectives

In this unit students will create their own experiment to observe the law of conservation of energy as one form of energy converts to another.

The objectives of this lesson are for students to:

- Explore the scientific method by creating their own experiment.
- Observe energy converting from one form to another.

Experiment

I. Think About It

Read this section of the *Laboratory Notebook* with your students.

Ask questions such as the following to guide open inquiry.

- *What are some examples of energy being converted from one form to another?*

- *Do you think energy being converted from one form to another is important for life? Why or why not?*

- *Do you think the energy that comes from the Sun is important for life on Earth? Is it ever converted? Why or why not?*

- *Do you think any energy conversions happen when a car is started and driven away? Why or why not? What are they?*

- *Do you think energy is being converted when water goes down a waterfall? How?*

- *Do you think that as energy gets converted from one form to another there is less and less energy on Earth? Why or why not?*

II. Experiment 5: On Your Own

Students will create their own experiment to explore the concept of the law of conservation of energy by observing how one form of energy changes to another. The goal is to convert different energies into other forms of energy and to include as many different forms of energy as they can.

Review with the students the different types of energy conversions described in Chapters 4 and 5 of the *Student Textbook*. Have them read the introduction to the experiment.

In the example given, the kinetic energy of a rolling marble is used to knock down a domino that has a cap filled with baking soda on top of it. The baking soda falls into vinegar and a chemical reaction occurs.

The marble begins with GPE which gets converted to KE as it rolls down the ramp. The KE is used to convert the GPE of the elevated baking soda into KE as it falls. This releases the chemical potential energy (CPE) in the baking soda and vinegar, and a chemical reaction begins, producing CO_2 which then puts out the fire. The chemical energy of the baking soda and vinegar is converted into heat energy and bubbles (gas). The gas rises and puts out the flame of a match.

Have the students think of ways this example might be changed. For example, the gas from the chemical reaction could be released into a small balloon or used to move a small piston.

❶-❷ Have students fill in the information requested.

❸ To prepare for the experiment, have the students do several "thought experiments" by asking themselves what different events they might include in their experiment that would change energy from one form to another. Some of their ideas will not be practical, but have them use their imagination to think of different ways to convert energy. Have them write down their ideas and identify what the energies will be before and after conversion.

❹ Once they have some different events in mind, they can think about ways to link the different ideas together in a series of events. Have them think about whether or not their ideas could work and what items they might use in their experiment.

The students will write an objective and hypothesis. Based on the series of events they have come up with, have them assemble a materials list, write down the steps of their experiment, make a drawing of their experimental setup. and then perform the experiment.

Have the students record their results whether or not their experiment worked. Have them write valid conclusions based on their results, and ask them what they might do differently next time.

III. Conclusions

Have the students review the results they recorded for the experiment. Have them draw conclusions based on the data they collected.

IV. Why?

Read this section of the *Laboratory Notebook* with your students.
Discuss any questions that might come up.

V. Just For Fun

Students will come up with a different setup for converting one form of energy to another. Encourage them to include more steps. They can use the same type of conversion as many times as they want and should also include some different types of conversions.

Experiment 6

Moving Marbles

Materials Needed

- several glass marbles of different sizes
- several steel marbles of different sizes
- cardboard tube, .7–1 meter [2.5–3 ft] long
- scissors
- black marking pen
- ruler
- letter scale or other small scale or balance

Objectives

In this experiment students will observe some properties of motion: inertia, friction, and momentum.

The objectives of this lesson are for students to:

- Observe that the motion of an object is changed when an outside force acts on the object.
- Observe how inertia, friction, and momentum together affect the motion of marbles.

Experiment

I. Think About It

Read this section of the *Laboratory Notebook* with your students.

Ask questions such as the following to guide open inquiry.

- *What do you think inertia is?*
- *Do you think you could play baseball without momentum? Why or why not?*
- *Where do you see friction occurring in day to day life?*
- *Do you think friction affects inertia? Why or why not?*
- *Do you think mass affects momentum? Why or why not?*

II. Experiment 6: Moving Marbles

Have the students read the entire experiment before writing an objective and a hypothesis.

Objective: Have the students write an objective. Some examples:

- *We will examine the movement of different marbles.*
- *We will investigate the momentum of different marbles.*
- *We will see what happens when one marble hits another.*
- *We will see if we can move a heavy marble with a light one.*

Hypothesis: Have the students write a hypothesis. Some examples:

- *The small glass marble will not be able to move the steel marble.*

- *The small glass marble will be able to move the steel marble.*

- *The small glass marble will stop when it hits the steel marble.*

- *The small glass marble will not stop when it hits the steel marble.*

EXPERIMENT

❶ Have the students weigh each marble. Have them label each marble with a number or letter or use the color of a marble as identification. Have them record the information for each marble in the chart provided in *Results—Part A*.

Remind the students that weight and mass are different and that they are not going to find the actual mass of the objects. However, they will be able to tell which objects have more mass—that is, those that weigh more. *(See Laboratory Notebook, Section IV. Why?)*

❷ Have the students take the cardboard tube, cut it in half lengthwise to make a trough, measure the length of the trough, and mark the halfway point with the black marking pen.

❸ Have the students measure .3 meter (1 foot) in both directions from the halfway mark and put a mark at each of these measurements. They will then have one mark on each side of the halfway mark.

❹ The cardboard trough should now have three marks: one at the halfway point, and one on either side of the halfway mark, .3 meter (1 foot) away from it. The trough will be used as a track for the marbles.

❺ Have the students roll the marbles one by one down the trough and notice how each one rolls. *(Does it roll straight? Is it easy to push off with your thumb? Does it pass the marks you drew?)* In the space provided in *Results—Part B*, have the students describe how each marble rolls. For example: *The glass marbles move easily down the trough and off the end. The small steel marbles move easily down the trough. The large steel marble takes more effort to get it to move down the trough.* (Answers will vary.)

Students may notice that it takes slightly less effort to push the glass marbles than the heavy steel marbles. This is because larger steel marbles have more inertia than smaller marbles.

❻-❼ Students will next place a glass marble on the center mark of the trough. Have the students roll a glass marble of the same size toward the marble in the center and observe the two marbles as they collide. Have them record their results in *Part C*.

Some example observations are: (Answers will vary.)

- *The rolling glass marble hit the other marble and stopped.*

- *The marble that was stopped started moving when it was hit by the rolling glass marble.*

Ask the students to observe the following:

- *When you roll the glass marble slowly, how far does the marble it hits move?*

- *When you roll the glass marble fast, how far does the marble it hits move?*

What they are observing here is the *conservation of momentum*—the total linear momentum (mass x speed) stays the same. However, because the rolling marble also has angular momentum (converted from linear momentum due to rotation) in addition to linear momentum, and also experiences friction, the stationary marble does not pick up quite all of the total linear momentum of the moving one. In the absence of angular momentum and friction, the total linear momentum of the moving marble would be transferred to the stationary marble. Despite this conversion of some of the linear momentum, the students should still be able to observe qualitatively that, when hit, the stationary marble will move faster when the rolling marble is traveling faster.

❽ Have the students repeat Steps ❻ and ❼ with different size marbles—rolling a heavy marble toward a light marble and a light marble toward a heavy marble.

Help them carefully observe what happens. They should observe that:

- *When the heavy marble impacts the light marble, the light marble will accelerate quite a bit.*

- *When the light marble impacts the heavy marble, the heavy marble will accelerate only a little bit.*

Have the students repeat this several times. Ask them what they think of their results. Have them record their results in *Results—Part D*.

Discuss the *conservation of momentum* which states that the total momentum stays the same. Remind the students that momentum is mass x speed. A large mass traveling at a certain speed will cause a smaller mass to accelerate to a faster speed, and a small mass traveling at a fast speed will accelerate a large mass to a slower speed. Because momentum is conserved, the total momentum will stay the same in each case.

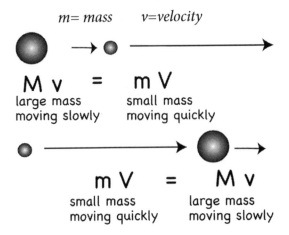

Although there is angular momentum in a rolling ball and friction is also present, the conservation of momentum should again be observable qualitatively in this part of the experiment.

III. Conclusions

Have the students review the results they recorded for the experiment. Have them draw conclusions based on the data they collected.

IV. Why?

Read this section of the *Laboratory Notebook* with your students.
Discuss any questions that might come up.

V. Just For Fun

Students will create their own experiment based on *Moving Marbles,* this time using a baseball, a basketball, and a golf ball. Have them think about whether they will have to make modifications to the experimental setup. Will they be able to use the cardboard trough? If not, how will they set up the experiment?

Have them record their results and draw conclusions about how differences in mass, inertia, momentum, speed, and friction affect this experiment.

Experiment 7

Accelerate to Win!

Materials Needed

- stopwatch
- compass
- an open space large enough to run (park, schoolyard, playground, backyard, etc.)
- 5 markers of students' choice to mark distances
- blank paper
- a group of friends

Objectives

In this experiment students will explore using basic math in physics formulas.

The objectives of this lesson are for students to:

- Learn how to calculate velocity and acceleration.
- Observe how velocity and acceleration vary over several trials.

Experiment

I. Think About It

Read this section of the *Laboratory Notebook* with your students.

Ask questions such as the following to guide open inquiry.

- *How fast is the fastest human?*
- *How fast is the fastest animal?*
- *How fast do you think you can run?*
- *Do you think you can train to run faster? Why or why not?*

II. Experiment 7: Accelerate to Win!

Have the students read the entire experiment before writing an objective and a hypothesis.

Objective: Have the students think of an objective for this experiment (What will they be learning?).

Hypothesis: Have the students write a hypothesis. The hypothesis can restate the objective in a statement that can be proved or disproved by their experiment. Some examples include:

- *I can run at a steady pace (velocity).*
- *I can accelerate at the end of each trial.*
- *My average velocity will increase with each trial.*

EXPERIMENT

❶ Help the students create a running track that is straight and has a manageable length. Have them mark a starting point and an ending point for the distance they will run. Make sure that when the total length of the track is divided into fourths, there will be enough time during the run for a timer to record the time of each segment of the run (one-fourth of the total track length).

❷ Have the students use a compass to determine in which direction they will be running and then record this direction in the chart in the *Results* section.

❸ Students will measure the length of the track using their own feet, walking heel-to-toe from the starting point to the finish with each step being one "foot." In the space provided, have them record the distance they measure.

❹ Using their measurement of the total distance to be run, students will calculate the distance of one-fourth of the track and then record this result for each of the time points d_1-d_4. This is the distance they will run for each of the four segments of the track.

❺ Have the students use their feet to measure the distance between the time points and mark each time point on the track in a way that the timer can see the mark as the runner is passing it.

❻-❼ One person will use a stopwatch to clock the times. Have them stand in a position where they will be able to see all the time points as the runner passes them. A second person will record the times in the *Laboratory Notebook*. Have your students run from the starting point to the finish line with the time keeper recording the time at each time point.

❽ Have the students run three or four times or until they are too tired to continue.

Results

❶-❷ Have your students calculate the velocity of each segment for each time trial and the acceleration between time points for each trial. Formulas are provided in the chart where students will record their answers. An example of calculations is included on the following page in this *Teacher's Manual*.

Space is provided for doing the calculations, but extra paper may be needed. If students use extra paper, have them fasten it in the *Laboratory Notebook* when they have completed the experiment.

A Place for Calculations (Calculations for example on next page)

Velocity

Trial 1: v_1 $\qquad v_1 = \dfrac{d_1}{t_1} = \dfrac{150 \text{ ft.}}{11 \text{ sec.}} = 13.6 \text{ ft./sec.}$

Trial 1: v_2 $\qquad v_2 = \dfrac{d_2}{t_2} = \dfrac{150 \text{ ft.}}{12 \text{ sec.}} = 12.5 \text{ ft./sec.}$

Trial 1: v_3 $\qquad v_3 = \dfrac{d_3}{t_3} = \dfrac{150 \text{ ft.}}{11 \text{ sec.}} = 13.6 \text{ ft./sec.}$

Trial 1: v_4 $\qquad v_4 = \dfrac{d_4}{t_4} = \dfrac{150 \text{ ft.}}{9 \text{ sec.}} = 16.7 \text{ ft./sec.}$

Acceleration*

Trial 1: $a_1 = \left(\dfrac{v_2 - v_1}{|t_2 - t_1|}\right) = \dfrac{12.5 - 13.6}{|12 - 11|} = \dfrac{-1.1 \text{ ft./sec.}}{1 \text{ sec.}} = -1.1 \text{ ft. sec.}^2 \text{ (squared)}$

Trial 1: $a_2 = \left(\dfrac{v_3 - v_2}{|t_3 - t_2|}\right) = \dfrac{13.6 - 12.5}{|11 - 12|} = \dfrac{1.1 \text{ ft./sec.}}{1 \text{ sec.}} = 1.1 \text{ ft. sec.}^2 \text{ (squared)}$

Trial 1: $a_3 = \left(\dfrac{v_4 - v_3}{|t_4 - t_3|}\right) = \dfrac{16.7 - 13.6}{|9 - 11|} = \dfrac{3.1 \text{ ft./sec.}}{2 \text{ sec.}} = 1.55 \text{ ft. sec.}^2 \text{ (squared)}$

Note: For acceleration, time is always a positive number. In the acceleration formula, the change in time (Δt) is written as $|t_f - t_i|$ to show that the result is expressed as a positive number.

Time Trial Results (Example—answers will vary)

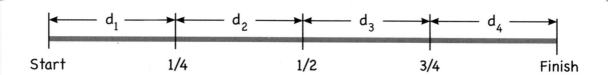

Start   1/4   1/2   3/4   Finish

Direction _____*north*_____

Distance (in "feet")

d_1 ___*150*___ d_2 ___*150*___ d_3 ___*150*___ d_4 ___*150*___

Time (seconds) t_1 t_2 t_3 t_4

	t_1	t_2	t_3	t_4
Trial 1	*11*	*12*	*11*	*9*
Trial 2				
Trial 3				

Velocity $v_1 = \dfrac{d_1}{t_1}$ $v_2 = \dfrac{d_2}{t_2}$ $v_3 = \dfrac{d_3}{t_3}$ $v_4 = \dfrac{d_4}{t_4}$

	v_1	v_2	v_3	v_4
Trial 1	*13.6 ft./sec.*	*12.5 ft./sec.*	*13.6 ft./sec.*	*16.7 ft./sec.*
Trial 2				
Trial 3				

Acceleration* $a_1 = \left(\dfrac{v_2 - v_1}{|t_2 - t_1|}\right)$ $a_2 = \left(\dfrac{v_3 - v_2}{|t_3 - t_2|}\right)$ $a_3 = \left(\dfrac{v_4 - v_3}{|t_4 - t_3|}\right)$

	a_1	a_2	a_3
Trial 1	*-1.1 ft. sec.^{2}*	*1.1 ft. sec.^{2}*	*1.55 ft. sec.^{2}*
Trial 2			
Trial 3			

*Note: For acceleration, time is always a positive number. In the acceleration formula, the change in time (Δt) is written as $|t_f - t_i|$ to show that the result is expressed as a positive number.

III. Conclusions

Have the students review the results they recorded for the experiment, answer the questions, and then draw conclusions based on their observations. Have them note if their conclusion supports or does not support their hypothesis.

IV. Why?

Read this section of the *Laboratory Notebook* with your students.
Discuss any questions that might come up.

Discuss with your students how they can measure their own velocity and acceleration by using time and distance. Explain how knowing these numbers can help a coach train an athlete for the Olympics. Have them discuss how this information might help them in a sport they participate in or how it might be used by participants in a sport they're interested in.

V. Just For Fun

Have the students run every day and record the date and amount of time they spend on each run. A chart is provided. They may find it interesting to create their own chart on a separate piece of paper that has a schedule for the runs and space to record the date and length of time of each run along with observations including how difficult or easy each run was, their route and its characteristics, the weather, etc. Do they notice a difference between the first and last training runs? What factors affect their runs?

After a few weeks have them repeat the experiment. Have them record and calculate their results and compare them to the first set of trials. What differences in the trials can they notice? Do they think running every day for a few weeks made a difference in the results? Has using the physics in this experiment helped them better understand how to run a race? Has it helped them observe a difference in their fitness? What conclusions can they draw?

Around and Around

Materials Needed

- pencil or pen
- marking pen
- thumbtack or pushpin
- 3 pieces of string—
  approximate sizes:
  10 cm [4 in.]
  15 cm [6 in.]
  20 cm [8 in.]
- tape
- ruler (metric)
- large piece of white paper
  (bigger than 30 cm [12 in.]
  square—students may need
  to tape several sheets of
  paper together)
- firm surface at least as large
  as the paper and that a
  thumbtack can be pinned into

Objectives

In this experiment students gain a better understanding of tangential speed and how it can be calculated mathematically.

The objectives of this lesson are for students to:

- Explore how math can be used to understand physics.
- Use math to calculate tangential speed.

Experiment

I. Think About It

Read this section of the *Laboratory Notebook* with your students.

Ask questions such as the following to guide open inquiry.

- *What does it feel like to ride on a playground merry-go-round? Why?*

- *As the merry-go-round is spinning, does it feel different if you sit near the center than if you sit near the outer edge? Why or why not?*

- *If you run in a circle around your room, how far do you go?*

- *If you run in a circle around your house, how far do you go? Is it farther than when you run around your room?*

- *How far do you think you would go if you could run around the Earth? the Sun? the solar system?*

- *If you could run around your house, the Earth, and the Sun, what speed do you think you would have to go to circle each in the same amount of time? Why?*

II. Experiment 8: Around and Around

Have the students read the entire experiment before writing an objective and a hypothesis.

Objective: Have the students think of an objective for this experiment (What will they be learning?).

Hypothesis: Have the students think about what they might learn from calculating the tangential speed of a circular path.

EXPERIMENT

❶ Have the students measure and cut the three lengths of string and, if necessary, tape together several sheets of white paper to a size larger than 30 cm [12 in.] square.

Provide a firm, flat surface at least as large as the paper and that a thumbtack or pushpin can be pinned into. Have the students fasten one end of the shortest string to the thumbtack or pushpin. Help them think about how this can be done; for example, making a loop in the string, making a knot at the end of the string, or wrapping the string around the thumbtack.

❷ Have the students use the marking pen to put a mark on the string at 5 cm (2 in.) from the thumbtack.

❸ Have the students place the pen or pencil at the 5 cm (2 in.) mark on the string, wrap the extra string around the pen and fasten it with tape.

❹-**❺** Have the students hold the thumbtack down so it doesn't dislodge and pull the pen away from the thumbtack until the string is stretched out to its full length. The pen should be held perpendicular as it is placed on the paper surface. Then have the students draw a circle with the thumbtack at the center. This will result in a 5 cm (2 in.) radius for the smallest circle.

❻ Have the students repeat Steps **❶**-**❺** with the other two pieces of string. For the middle size string the pen will be 10 cm (4 in.) from the thumbtack, and for the longest piece of string the pen will be 15 cm (6 in.) from the thumbtack.

Results

A table is provided with formulas for calculating the circumference of the circles and the tangential speed (see next page).

❶ Have the students measure the radius of each circle. Point out that the radius is the same as the length of the string. Have them record the radii in the table.

❷ Have the students calculate the circumference. They are provided with the equation: $c = 2\pi r$.

❸ Have the students calculate the tangential speeds using the circumference of each circle and assuming one rotation takes 1 minute (1 RPM).

Calculating Tangential Speed

	①	②	③
String Length	5 cm	10 cm	15 cm

Circle:

	①	②	③
Radius	*5 cm*	*10 cm*	*15 cm*

Calculate the Circumference [π (pi) = 3.14]

①	②	③
$c = 2\pi r$ $c = 2\pi r \cdot$ *5 cm* $c =$ *31.4 cm*	$c = 2\pi r$ $c = 2\pi r \cdot$ *10 cm* $c =$ *62.8 cm*	$c = 2\pi r$ $c = 2\pi r \cdot$ *15 cm* $c =$ *94.2 cm*

Circumference	*31.4 cm*	*62.8 cm*	*94.2 cm*

Calculate the tangential speed for one revolution (1 RPM)

Tangential speed = distance traveled/time

> Note: Distance traveled is one revolution—the circumference of the circle (c).
>
> Time (t) equals one minute for this problem.

Tangential speed (S_T) = c/t

Calculation

①	②	③
$S_T = c/t$ $S_T =$ *31.4* /t	$S_T = c/t$ $S_T =$ *62.8* /t	$S_T = c/t$ $S_T =$ *94.2* /t

Tangential Speed	*31.4 cm/min.*	*62.8 cm/min.*	*94.2 cm/min.*

III. Conclusions

Have the students answer the questions and draw a conclusion based on their observations. Note if their conclusion supports or does not support their hypothesis.

IV. Why?

Read this section of the *Laboratory Notebook* with your students.

Discuss with your student how using mathematics helps us explain many of the phenomena we experience in the real world, such as spinning on a merry-go-round.

Discuss any questions that might come up.

V. Just For Fun

Have your students think of some different objects that show tangential speed when in motion and list these objects in the space provided.

Next, have them think of a way to calculate the tangential speed of one of these objects. For example, a tape measure can be used to measure the radius at different points from the center of a merry-go-round. The radii can then be plugged into the equation provided.

Experiment 9

Power Pennies

Materials Needed

- 10-20 copper pennies (pennies made before 1982 have more copper and work best)
- aluminum foil
- paper towels
- salt water: 30-45 ml (2-3 Tbsp.) salt per 240 ml (1 cup) water
- voltmeter*
- 2 plastic-coated copper wires, each 10-15 cm (4"-6") long
- duct tape (or other strong tape)
- scissors
- wire cutters
- fine steel wool, plain (no soap), 1 pad
- 9 volt battery
- ovenproof pan or dish
- heatproof pad or surface

*An inexpensive voltmeter can be purchased at any store that supplies electrical equipment. Carefully read the instructions for the voltmeter. Make sure that the voltmeter is set to "voltage" and that the voltage scale is low enough to detect small voltages. A typical penny-cell produces about 0.5v.

Optional

- wire stripping tool
- bucket of water

Objectives

In this experiment students will learn about how chemical potential energy converts to electrical energy and becomes usable.

The objectives of this lesson are for students to:

- Make a model battery that converts chemical potential energy to electrical energy.
- Collect data in a chart and plot it on a graph.

Experiment

I. Think About It

Read this section of the *Laboratory Notebook* with your students.

Ask questions such as the following to guide open inquiry.

- *Where do you think chemical energy comes from? Why?*

- *How would you explain chemical potential energy?*

- *Have you ever used a device that converted chemical potential energy to another form of energy? What was the device and how did it work?*

- *Do you think metals can be used to generate electrical energy? Why or why not?*

- *What do you think the world would be like if there were no stored energy? Why?*

- *Do you think the invention of the battery was important? Why or why not? How do you think it would change our lives if there were no batteries?*

II. Experiment 9: Power Pennies

Have the students read the entire experiment before writing an objective and a hypothesis.

Objective: Have the students write an objective (What will they be learning?). Some examples:

- *To discover how a simple voltaic cell operates.*

- *To construct a voltaic battery and measure voltages.*

- *To see if pennies, aluminum, and saltwater can really make electricity.*

Hypothesis: Have the students write a hypothesis. Some examples:

- *Pennies, aluminum foil, and salt water will not generate electricity.*

- *Pennies, aluminum foil, and salt water will make electricity.*

- *More layers in the voltaic cell will generate more electricity.*

EXPERIMENT

❶-❷ Have the students scrub the pennies with steel wool to remove oxidation and dirt. Then have them cut out up to 20 penny-size circles from aluminum foil and paper towel. It is important that the cutouts be very close to the size of a penny.

❸ Have them soak the paper towel circles in the salt water.

❹ Help them strip the plastic coating off both ends of one of the pieces of wire, using wire cutters or a wire stripper to carefully cut through the plastic without cutting the metal wire. Have them tape one end of the exposed wire to a penny.

❺ Have the students strip the plastic off the ends of the second piece of wire and tape the exposed metal at one end of the wire to a circle of aluminum foil.

❻ Students will begin by stacking the pieces. Have them place the circle of aluminum foil on a firm surface with the attached wire touching the surface. Then have them put one of the wet paper towel circles on top of the aluminum foil followed by the penny that has the wire taped to it, wire side up. (The paper towel piece should be wet but not dripping.) This makes one cell of the battery. It should look like this:

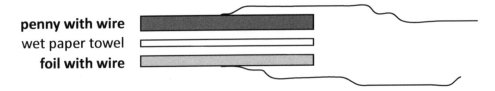

| penny with wire |
| wet paper towel |
| foil with wire |

❼ Have the students take the battery wires and connect them to the leads (wires) of the voltmeter, switch the voltmeter to "voltage," and in the *Results* section record the number it shows. This is the amount of voltage the single cell battery produces. Make sure the voltmeter is set to "voltage" and that the voltage scale is low enough to detect small voltages. A typical penny-cell produces about 0.5v.

❽ Have the students add another cell to the battery and record the voltage. (A cell is a foil layer, a paper layer, and a penny layer.) The penny with the wire and the aluminum foil with the wire will remain as the "ends" of the battery. Additional cells will be added in between these two ends.

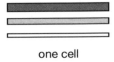

one cell

The battery now has two cells and should look like this.

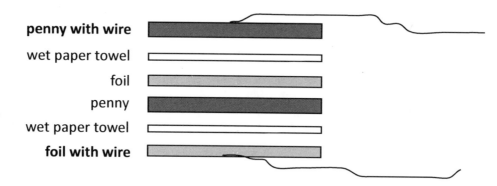

penny with wire
wet paper towel
foil
penny
wet paper towel
foil with wire

Have the students check the voltage and record the amount in the *Results* section.

❾ The students should add as many additional cells as they can, recording the voltage each time a new cell is added..

If the voltage fluctuates (appears to increase and then decrease), have the students examine their battery to see if there is a short circuit. A short circuit will occur in spots where the paper towel or aluminum foil is enough larger than the penny that it hangs down to touch a lower layer. The electric current will find the shortest distance through the battery by using these touching layers and thus missing parts of the cells.

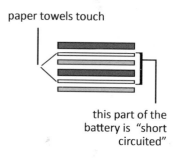

paper towels touch

this part of the battery is "short circuited"

Results

Have the students plot the data they collected, making a graph with "Voltage" on the x-axis (horizontal) and "Number of Cells" on the y-axis (vertical).

Have the students discuss their data. They should observe that, overall, as the number of cells increases, the voltage increases. If the battery had a short circuit, they would have seen the voltage fluctuate after they added a cell.

Have the students discuss possible sources of error.

III. Conclusions

Have the students review the results they recorded for the experiment. Have them draw conclusions based on the data they collected.

IV. Why?

Read this section of the *Laboratory Notebook* with your students.
Discuss any questions that might come up.

V. Just For Fun

Steel Wool Meets Battery

In this experiment students will touch the terminals of a 9 volt battery to steel wool. Students should be supervised while performing this experiment because the steel wool will burn. This is not a dangerous experiment, but as a precaution it is best performed outside away from things that could catch fire and it requires that a little care be taken.

Materials

9 volt battery
fine steel wool, plain (no soap)—coarse steel wool probably won't work
ovenproof pan or dish
heatproof pad or surface

Optional: have a bucket of water on hand in case of accident

Experiment

Students are instructed to have an adult help with this experiment.

❶ Have the students take a piece of steel wool and spread it out with their fingers until it is a loose ball. The amount of steel wool, how fine it is, and how it is spread out will affect the results of the experiment.

❷ Have the students place the steel wool ball in an ovenproof pan and place the pan on a heatproof pad or heatproof surface. It is possible for the pan to get very hot.

❸ Have the students hold the 9 volt battery at the bottom and touch the terminals to the steel wool, being careful that their fingers are away from the steel wool. It should ignite with just a brief touch. If not, have the students repeat. Caution them not to touch the pan as it may become very hot, depending on how the steel wool burns. Students can blow on or fan the steel wool to make it burn faster.

❹ Have students record their observations in the space provided.

Why did what happened happen?

Have the students reach and record conclusions. They can send a summary of their conclusions about why the steel wool burned to:
office@gravitaspublications.com.

If they are right, we'll send a surprise item to them.

Experiment 10

Charge It!

Materials Needed

- small glass jar with lid
- aluminum foil (small piece)
- paperclip
- duct tape (or other strong tape)
- plastic or rubber rod (or balloon)
- silk fabric (or can use hair with a balloon)
- scissors
- ruler
- awl or other tool to make a hole
- several thin, bendable plastic straws (thick straws may not work well)
- paper tissues (Kleenex) or cloth made of silk or wool
- small piece of paper
- small piece of aluminum foil
- 1 or more books—thin pages preferable
- 1-2 plastic combs
- plastic cup
- shallow bowl or a plate

Objectives

In this experiment students will explore electrostatic force.

The objectives of this lesson are for students to:

- Observe how like electrical forces repel.
- Observe that electrons can be transferred from one object to another.

Experiment

I. Think About It

Read this section of the *Laboratory Notebook* with your students.
Ask questions such as the following to guide open inquiry.

- *What parts of an atom do you think are charged? What charge do they carry?*

- *How do you think an object gets an electric charge?*

- *Do you think your hair can become electrically charged? Why or why not?*

- *How do you think opposite charges interact? Charges that are alike?*

- *What do you think electrical force is and what does it do?*

II. Experiment 10: Charge It!

Have the students read the entire experiment before writing an objective and a hypothesis.

Objective: Have the students write an objective (What will they be learning?). Some examples:

- *We will build an instrument to detect electric charge.*

- *We will test for electric charge with an electroscope.*

Hypothesis: Have the students guess what might happen with the electroscope. Give them the hint that the two pieces of aluminum foil will carry the same charge. Then ask what the aluminum foil will do.

Have the students write a hypothesis. Some examples:

- *The aluminum foil pieces will separate in the electroscope.*

- *The aluminum foil pieces will stick to each other in the electroscope.*

EXPERIMENT

❶ Have the students cut two narrow strips of aluminum foil of equal length (about 2.5 cm [1 inch] long).

❷ Help the students poke a small hole in the center of the lid of the glass jar.

❸ Have students bend open a paperclip to make a right angle from the outer loop of wire and a small hook from the inner loop. (See illustration on right.)

❹ Students are to place the straight part of the paperclip through the small hole in the jar lid from the bottom side of the lid, and then bend and secure the paper clip to the lid with strong tape, leaving the end of the paper clip exposed.

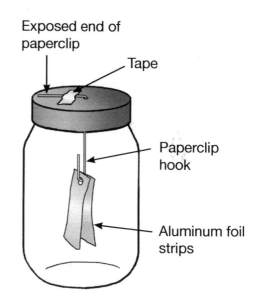

Exposed end of paperclip

Tape

Paperclip hook

Aluminum foil strips

❺ Have the students hang the two strips of aluminum foil from the hook that is on the underside of the jar lid and place the lid on the jar with the aluminum foil hanging from the hook inside the jar.

They have now made an electroscope.

❻ To build up an electric charge, have the students rub the plastic or rubber rod with silk fabric or rub the balloon in their hair or on the cat.

❼ Have them gently touch the rod or the balloon to the end of the paper clip that is on the outside of the jar lid.

❽ Have the students observe the two pieces of aluminum foil and record their results in the space provided in the *Results* section. They can use drawings and/or words.

Students should see the pieces of foil separate. Have them think about the following:

- *What would happen if you touched your fingers to the end of the paperclip?*

- *How long will the charge last?*

- *Are there things that would make the aluminum foil separate farther? More rubbing? Different plastic rod? A glass rod? A metal rod?*

Results

Space is provided for recording observations.

III. Conclusions

Have the students review the results they recorded for the experiment. Have them draw conclusions based on the data they collected.

IV. Why?

Read this section of the *Laboratory Notebook* with your students.
Discuss any questions that might come up.

V. Just For Fun

These are some fun, simple experiments that demonstrate electrostatic force. A low humidity environment is needed for these to work well. For each experiment students will need to charge one or two plastic straws or plastic combs by rubbing with a paper tissue or cloth made of silk or wool. A student may need a helper to be able to charge more than one object so they don't accidentally discharge the first one while charging the second.

Have students record their observations after each experiment. Space is provided at the end of the section.

The instructions here are minimal with no illustrations to encourage students to figure out for themselves how to work the experiments.

▶ Have the students cut some very small pieces of paper and aluminum. Ask them to discuss what they think will happen when they put a charged straw near these pieces and how close they think the straw will have to get for this to happen. If nothing happens, ask them to think about why it may not have worked and what they might do differently. Have them try it again using their ideas. The straw should attract some of the paper and foil pieces.

▶ Have the students see if they can use a charged straw to turn a page in a book. A book with thinner pages may work better, and students can try different books. Have them see if holding the book at different angles helps.

► In this experiment students will see how electrostatic force will affect a stream of water. Have them turn on a faucet so a thin stream of water is coming out. Have them charge a plastic comb. Ask them to discuss what they think will happen as they move the charged comb slowly toward the water and what they think will happen if they move the comb around or wiggle it or if they use two charged combs. If nothing happens, ask them what they might do differently and then have them try it.

Have them repeat the experiment with a charged straw, two charged straws, and a comb and a straw together. Ask them what they observed in each of these cases.

► Have the students bend two straws slightly, then charge them. Next they will hold one in each hand by the short part so the long parts are parallel and upright. Ask them what they think will happen as they move the straws close together. The straws will have like charges, so the students should be able to observe them repelling each other.

► Here the students will charge two straws and hold them so they are parallel to the floor and aligned one above the other with their hands one above the other. Ask them what they think will happen as they move the straws closer together or farther apart. Again the straws will have like charges and will repel. Have them hold the top straw loosely—just enough to keep it aligned over the bottom one and not swinging from side to side. This will allow it to move as it is repelled.

► Here students will make an electric charge indicator. Have them put just enough water in a shallow bowl or plate that a plastic cup will float a bit and be able to move around. Have them charge one end of a straw and place the straw on top of the cup (across the rim). Ask them what they think will happen if they charge another straw and bring it close to the straw that's on the cup. What if they move the straw they're holding around? They can continue to experiment with a charged comb to see if they get different results, and then try different combinations of straws and combs. Have them charge the whole straw that's on the cup instead of just one end and see if anything different happens.

► Ask the students what other electrostatic experiments they can think of on their own.

Experiment 11

Circuits and Ohm's Law

Materials Needed

- (2) D cell batteries and battery holder
- (2) 3.7 volt light bulbs and sockets
- (1) switch
- (4) alligator clip connectors
- (2) 5 ohm, 1/4 watt resistors
- (1) DC motor with propeller

Materials are available as a kit from Home Science Tools (as of this writing):
Product #: EL-KITBASC
http://www.hometrainingtools.com/

Objectives

In this experiment students will explore electrical circuits, current, and resistance.

The objectives of this lesson are for students to:

- Create electrical circuits.
- Observe how resistors and an open or closed switch affect an electrical circuit.

Experiment

I. Think About It

Read this section of the *Laboratory Notebook* with your students.

Ask questions such as the following to guide open inquiry.

> - *How would you describe an electric current?*
>
> - *How do you think an electric current can be used?*
>
> - *How long does it take a light bulb to light up once the switch is turned on? Why?*
>
> - *What do you think would happen if you took an extension cord, made the cord very long, and plugged a power drill into it? How long would it take to start the drill? Why? Does the length of the cord matter? Why or why not?*
>
> - *Do you think the only way to get an electric current is to plug something into an outlet? Why or why not?*
>
> - *Where do you think the electric current in your house comes from?*

II. Experiment 11: Circuits and Ohm's Law

Have the students read the entire experiment before writing an objective and a hypothesis.

Objective: Have the students write an objective (What will they be learning?). Some examples:

> - *We will find out if resistors change how electricity works.*
>
> - *We will observe electric current and find out what happens if a switch is open.*

Hypothesis: Have the students write a hypothesis. Some examples:

- *A resistor will not affect the electric flow.*

- *An open switch will keep the light bulb from lighting.*

EXPERIMENT

Symbols to be used in circuit diagrams

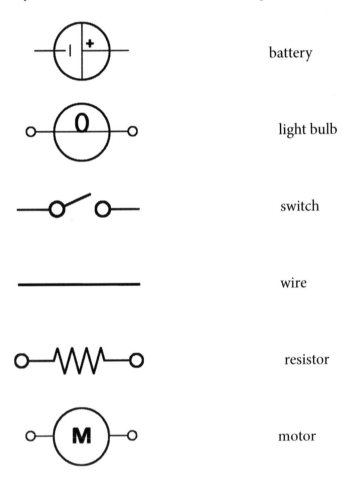

battery

light bulb

switch

wire

resistor

motor

Part I

❶ In the space provided, have the students use the above symbols to draw a diagram of a simple circuit that includes a battery as the source of electricity, a light bulb, and a switch. Their diagram should look something like the following:

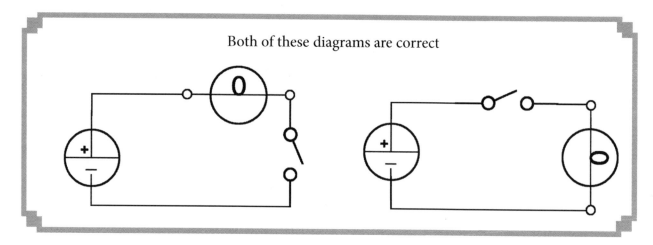

Both of these diagrams are correct

❷ Have the students follow their diagram to build a circuit. Have them record their observations in the space provided.

❸ Have the students repeat Step ❶, drawing another circuit, this time adding the DC motor.

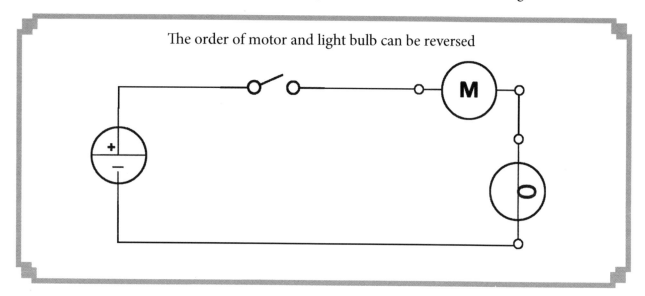

The order of motor and light bulb can be reversed

❹ Have the students build the circuit, close and open the switch, and record their observations.

Part II: Testing Ohm's Law

❶ Have the students build a circuit according to the diagram shown in the *Laboratory Notebook* (see following illustration). Have them close the switch, note the brightness of the bulb, and record their observations.

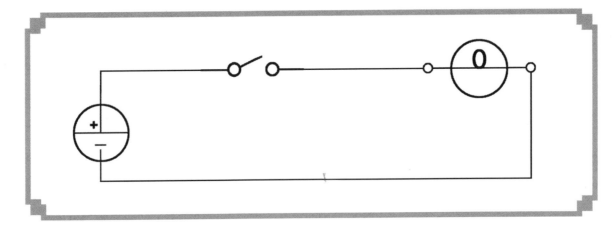

❷ Have the students open the switch and insert a resistor between the light bulb and the battery. Have them draw their circuit, then close the switch and observe the brightness of the light bulb. Have them record their observations.

The resistor can go on either side of the light bulb.

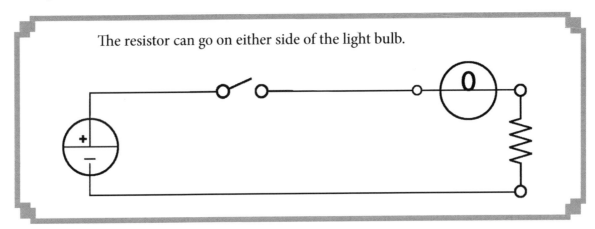

❸ Have the students open the switch and insert a second resistor next to the first one. They may need to wrap or bend the end wires of the resistors together to get a good connection. Have them draw their circuit, then close the switch, observe the brightness of the light bulb, and record their observations. Their circuit should look something like the following.

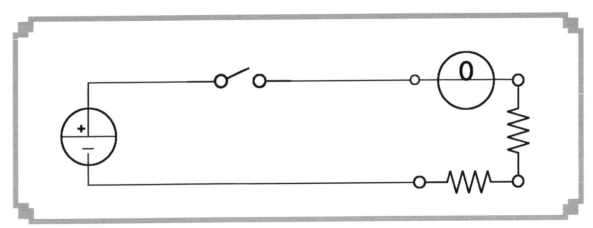

Notes about Results

When the students place a resistor between the light bulb and the battery, they should find that the light coming from the light bulb is dimmer than it was without the resistor.

They should notice that the bulb does not light up when they add a second resistor to the circuit. Explain to them that the resistors are behaving like kinks in a hose. They are cutting off some of the flow of electrons like a kink in a hose cuts off some of the flow of water. The more resistors added to the circuit, the dimmer the light from the bulb will become as fewer and fewer electrons can flow through the wire. If enough resistance is added to the circuit, there will be too few electrons flowing to light the bulb.

III. Conclusions

Have the students review the results they recorded for the experiment. Have them draw conclusions based on the data they collected.

IV. Why?

Read this section of the *Laboratory Notebook* with your students.
Discuss any questions that might come up.

V. Just For Fun

Students are to create a parallel circuit that includes two light bulbs. Have them draw their circuit and record their observations.

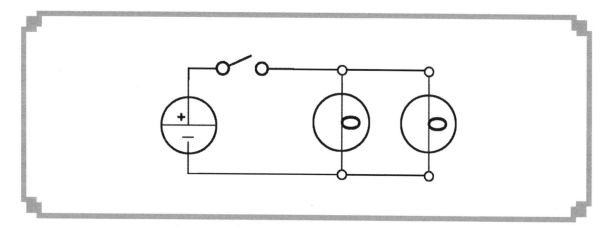

Have them continue to experiment by using the materials they have on hand to build different circuits of their own design. Have them draw the circuit and record the results each time. When they have completed the experiment, have them write their conclusions.

Experiment 12

Wrap It Up!

Materials Needed

- metal rod (a large nail such as an 8.9 cm [3.5"] long 16d flathead nail or an unmagnetized screwdriver can be used)
- electrical wire, .3–.6 meter (1'–2')
- 10–20 paperclips
- 6v or larger battery (use a 12v battery if a screwdriver is used)
- electrical tape or 2 alligator clips
- scissors
- wire cutters
- bar magnet
- small plastic baggie
- small flat-bottomed clear plastic container with lid [about 5 cm x 8 cm x 1.5 cm (2" x 3" x 1/2")—a box straight pins come in would work)
- clear Karo syrup, small amount
- spoon
- 2 pencils or other props

Optional

- wire stripping tool
- iron filings (available from Home Science Tools CH-IRON http://www.hometrainingtools.com/

Objectives

In this experiment students will be introduced to electromagnets.

The objectives of this lesson are for students to:

- Explore making an electromagnet.
- Observe how an electric current can be used to create magnetic force.

Experiment

I. Think About It

Read this section of the *Laboratory Notebook* with your students.

Ask questions such as the following to guide open inquiry.

- *How do you think magnetic force is created in a magnet?*

- *What is the rule that applies to both electric charges and magnetic poles?*

- *Do you think that knowing how magnetic poles react to each other could be useful? Why or why not?*

- *Do you think a magnetic field affects the space that surrounds the magnet? How can you tell?*

- *Do you think a magnet can ever be turned off? Why or why not?*

- *Do you think a magnet can cause another object to become magnetic? Why or why not?*

II. Experiment 12: Wrap It Up!

Have the students read the entire experiment before writing an objective and a hypothesis.

Objective: Have the students write an objective (What will they be learning?). Some examples:

- *In this experiment we will build an electromagnet.*

- *In this experiment we will explore the properties of electromagnets.*

Hypothesis: Have the students write a hypothesis. Some examples:

- *It won't matter how many coils we use, we won't be able to pick up more than a few paperclips.*

- *The more coils that are wrapped around the rod, the stronger the electromagnet.*

- *The number of paperclips we pick up will be proportional to the number of coils in the electromagnet.*

EXPERIMENT

❶ Have the students cut the electrical wire so that it is .3-.6 meter (1-2 feet) long.

❷-❹ Have them remove the plastic coating off the ends of the wire, exposing about 6 mm (1/4 inch) of metal on each end of the wire. Then have them tape one end of the wire to the positive (+) terminal of the battery and the other end of the wire to the negative (-) terminal of the battery. (Alligator clips may be used in place of tape.)

Whenever the wire is connected to both the + and - terminals, the battery is running down, so the wire should be disconnected when the battery is not in use.

❺ Before wrapping the wire around the rod, have the students touch the rod to a pile of paperclips and note whether any paperclips are picked up by the rod. Have them record their results in the chart in the *Results* section.

❻ Have the students coil the wire around the metal rod a few times, making sure both ends of the wire remain hooked to the battery or reattaching them if they come off.

❼ Have the students touch the metal rod to the paperclips, count the coils and the number of paperclips picked up, and record their results.

❽-❾ Have them wrap another 1 to 5 coils around the metal rod, touch the end of the metal rod to the paperclips, and record their results.

❿ Have the students continue adding coils to the metal rod, counting the number of paperclips that are picked up, and recording the results each time they increase the number of coils. When all the data has been collected, have the students plot the data on a graph.

Results

Have the students record the results of each step of the experiment and then graph the data. Results may vary, but there should be an overall trend—as the number of coils increases, the number of paper clips the electromagnet can pick up also increases.

Using a 12v battery, one student got these results.

Number of Coils	Number of Paper Clips
0	0
10	0-very weak
15	1
20	2
25	8
30	12
35	15

III. Conclusions

Looking at the graph, have the students discuss their results and draw conclusions based on the data they collected. Help them discuss any sources of error they might have encountered.

IV. Why?

Read this section of the *Laboratory Notebook* with your students.
Discuss any questions that might come up.

V. Just For Fun

Seeing the Magnetic Field

In this experiment students will collect iron filings that occur naturally in soil and use them to observe magnetic field lines. If it isn't possible for iron filings to be collected outside, they can be purchased.

❶ Have the students place a bar magnet in a small plastic baggie and take it and the plastic container outside where there is exposed dirt. Have them swirl the baggie containing the magnet in the dirt to collect iron filings on the outside of the baggie.

❷ Have them place the baggie with the magnet inside in the plastic container and then remove the magnet from the baggie. The iron filings should fall off the outside of the baggie and into the container.

❸ Have them repeat Steps ❶-❷ several times until the iron filings make a thin layer in the box. Enough iron filings need to be gathered that when the electromagnet is placed under the container, the magnetic field lines formed by the iron filings will be obvious.

❹-❺ Have the students pour enough Karo syrup into the container to just cover the iron filings and then carefully place the container over the electromagnet they built previously. They will need to prop up the ends of the plastic container to keep it flat.

❻-❼ Have the students turn on the electromagnet, observe the iron filings for several minutes, and record their conclusions in the space provided.

More REAL SCIENCE-4-KIDS Books
by Rebecca W. Keller, PhD

Building Blocks Series yearlong study program—each Student Textbook has accompanying Laboratory Notebook, Teacher's Manual, Lesson Plan, Study Notebook, Quizzes, and Graphics Package

Exploring Science Book K (Activity Book)
Exploring Science Book 1
Exploring Science Book 2
Exploring Science Book 3
Exploring Science Book 4
Exploring Science Book 5
Exploring Science Book 6
Exploring Science Book 7
Exploring Science Book 8

Focus On Series unit study program—each title has a Student Textbook with accompanying Laboratory Notebook, Teacher's Manual, Lesson Plan, Study Notebook, Quizzes, and Graphics Package

Focus On Elementary Chemistry
Focus On Elementary Biology
Focus On Elementary Physics
Focus On Elementary Geology
Focus On Elementary Astronomy

Focus On Middle School Chemistry
Focus On Middle School Biology
Focus On Middle School Physics
Focus On Middle School Geology
Focus On Middle School Astronomy

Focus On High School Chemistry

Super Simple Science Experiments

21 Super Simple Chemistry Experiments
21 Super Simple Biology Experiments
21 Super Simple Physics Experiments
21 Super Simple Geology Experiments
21 Super Simple Astronomy Experiments
101 Super Simple Science Experiments

Note: A few titles may still be in production.

Gravitas Publications Inc.
www.gravitaspublications.com
www.realscience4kids.com

GRAVITAS
PUBLICATIONS